OWANN KHRON

the ElseWheRe CHRONICLES

BOOK TWO
THE SHADOW SPIES

ART
BANNISTER

STORY
NYKKO

COLORS
JAFFRÉ

GRAPHIC UNIVERSE™ • MINNEAPOLIS

ThANk you to my pARENts foR their unfAiliNg suppoRt.

ThANk you to DeNis ANd LauReNce foR theiR
sensible editoRiAl Advice ANd the 24-houR hotliNe.

ThANk you to my sweet FloRA, without whom this book,
At least the ARt, would be oNly A shAdow of itself.

ANd Next, thANks Also to the otheR two guys,
because they've doNe A gReAt job too.

—BANNisteR

To SAbiNe, Léo, ANd Noé
—Nykko

To MAthilde, ANd thANk you foR youR help!
—JAffRé

I am going to give you a map on which your grandfather Gabriel marked the locations of the other passageways.

He built them to make his long expeditions easier.

Wherever he explored, he was never more than five days' walk from one of them.

How do you know he didn't close them off, like the one in the cave?

Even if the Master of Shadows terrified him...

...Gabriel would never have separated our two worlds after joining them together. I know that there still exists a working passageway.

BABUMP!
ZWIP
ROLL PLOP BOP!
ROLL

Put me down, my boy. This is where we must part.

But would he really have risked marking the passageways on a map?

Perhaps not, Rebecca! All the same, do not give up trying to find one.

One last thing, my children. Watch out for the stalking Shadows. They are enslaved to the Master of Shadows—they are his *spies*, and they are very vicious.

You have saved the spirit of your grandfather. *Ilmahil* will come to your aid.

They fear the light, of course, but they lurk in the darkest places. Do not for any reason stray from the trail!

The time has come for us to say farewell.

In this bag, you will find things belonging to your grandfather, which he entrusted to me in secret.

Carry these back to your world. If Gabriel kept them hidden, then it was because they are a danger to us here.

You will also find the map with the passageways marked on it.

The nearest passageway is in Zumas, three days' walk from here. You absolutely must hide at night.

Gabriel planned ahead and built shelters along the way. You should reach the first one by this evening.

5

What **are** they?

SCHLURP

GULLCH

GLURSH

SCHLUR

CLACK

Don't just stand there, Reb!

Run!

KPOW

WHOOSH

SPLAT

PLASH

BASH

I can't hold them off for long!

Get up!

BONK

PLOP

This map is useless until we've found the trail.

It's too late, anyway—it's going to be night soon.

I don't like to say this, but we'll have to spend the night here. So much for finding the shelter.

At least we won't be cold.

Oh, you have a lighter?

I got it off my stupid brother.

You *smoke?*

Not yet.

You want to try it? It's my first time too.

I don't think that's such a good idea, Max.

Ugh... you really have to be hungry to get that stuff down.

Seriously, you *like* that?

Yeah, it's a nice change from canned stuff and pizza. Plus, it actually tastes good.

Your parents never feed you anything but canned food and pizza?

There's just my mom, and she never cooks.

I like it!! The inside is nice and crunchy.

Max, you must be exaggerating.

With my brothers, once, I made a rum cake for Mom's birthday.

But since there wasn't any rum, I used one of the bottles of wine she always hides under her bed.

She was so angry, she hit me in the head. I was only four years old too.

Why are you telling me this?

Look, here's the scar.

Because now it's your turn to tell me your worst memory. The one that made you so scared last night in the cave.

The light-rifle! I've lost the light-rifle!

Stay near the fire! That'll keep it away!

A Shadow Spy!

Yes, but for how long?

Back off!

Uh oh...I shouldn't have done that.

The fire is going out!

AAH!

TAP

Don't panic, Theo. They're friends.

They helped me carry you here.

You were knocked out cold when the cave collapsed on us. We barely got out of there, you know.

These little raisin buns are super good. Maybe a little too sweet.

Lookit the teeth on Popeye here!

At least we know he isn't a cannibal. Heh heh heh…

How can you joke around in our situation?

Hm?

Perhaps laughter is a good way to combat fear.

Huh?

Let me see to your arm, son.

Teo kranal agadamgorodok! Em khron pelmek onne.

Uh...

It is as I thought. A Shadow Spy touched you not long ago.

It just brushed me...two days ago.

You were lucky. But the sickness is spreading.

We must work fast.

Why? What's going to happen to him?

Nothing. We are going to take care of him.

What, with *maggots?* Yuck!

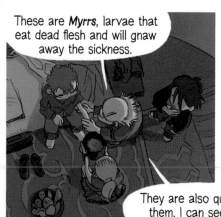

These are *Myrrs*, larvae that eat dead flesh and will gnaw away the sickness.

Urk!

They are also quite delicious if you grill them. I can see you like them a lot.

I am going to cover it with a salve.

Their slime has curative properties.

When it has completely dried up, you can peel it off.

You are very lucky indeed. Another half day more and we would not have been able to save you.

Now, my children, you must prepare to leave.

You're kicking us out?

If it's because I made fun of you... a little... I'm sorry.

Who is this Popeye... some sort of village idiot?

No! He's strong and brave and—

Then you paid me a compliment!

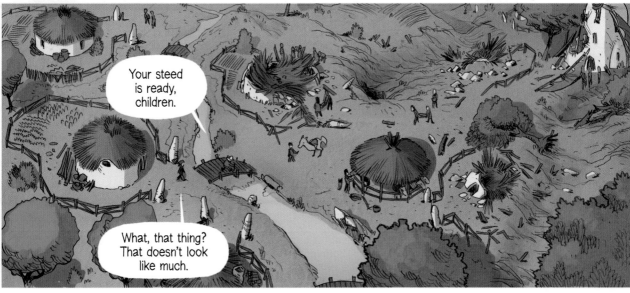

Your steed is ready, children.

What, that thing? That doesn't look like much.

It is a *Zhin!* Thanks to him, you should be able to catch up with Max and Rebecca, who are a day ahead of you.

You've seen Max and Reb?!

Then... they're alive!

They are on their way to find another passageway.

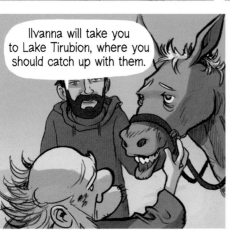

Ilvanna will take you to Lake Tirubion, where you should catch up with them.

After that, you must fend for yourselves!

Ilmahil tara kol auss!

I hear you, Max. But I don't care. I'm dirty.

I feel lousy. I need a good bath.

And a bath wouldn't hurt *you,* either.

Hey. What do *you* want from me?

SPLORTCH!

Ulp—

Hahahaha! You don't have a choice, now!

Everybody in the pool!

I don't know if I should be happy or scared that the horse-thing dumped us in the middle of nowhere at nightfall.

You know, wasn't Ilvanna supposed to control that beast?

You've got some nerve, Noah! We wouldn't be in this mess if you hadn't gotten the *stupid* idea to *whip* that *stupid* animal.

Yeah, well, haven't you ever seen cowboys spur their horses to make them go faster?

And what makes you think we're in a Western?

I don't see any cowboys here, do you? And the cavalry isn't going to rescue us.

We're in a *horror movie!*

Are you done?

LIGHT!! LIGHT!!

See! What'd I tell you?

What should we do?

Take these two flashballs!

LIGHT!!

We've gotta hide!

Veray dalga, trekall! Es Krhon!

Move fast!

SHLOK

I can't hold them back for long!

SHLOK

Yahoo! The cavalry!

Vlish!

Wow, what a girl.

Isn't that a little weird, just taking off like that?

Maybe she has something more important to do.

Yeah, well, that doesn't help us much.

I think I'm smitten...

Yeah, he's bitten, all right.

Poor Doleann! Now I know why she left so fast.

Hey!

Wait for me!

All the same, she abandoned us pretty quickly.

I'd like to know more about this mysterious girl who speaks our language.

Ick, these bugs are all over me!

That's right— she does. I didn't even notice that.

Tiraak! Tiraak!

Leave me alone!

What's up with Ilvanna? The butterflies are pretty.

Ow! It bit me!

Theo! Don't touch them!

Bit you where? Let me see.

Hey, what's that?

I know, it's kinda gross. But if you believe the nice old man who put it there, it saved my life.

Are you talking about Norgavol? The old man who speaks English?

Yeah. I think I can take it off, now.

Nobody would believe that the Shadow touched me in Grandpa Gabe's library.

Then my arm started to smell bad.

I hope the old man knew what he was doing.

Yahoo! He healed me! I'm saved!

Teo graal ter betawol.

Hahahaha! It's terrific, Ilvanna!

Betawol! Es graal ter betawol!

The old man saved me! Thank you, old man!

Theo!

Hey!

It's because of the butterfly!

Ilvanna tried to warn us.

We've lost a lot of time.

You want me to take over?

S'okay.

LIGHT! LIGHT!

Oh no, not this again!

Per mel, vlish!

Hurry up!

Faster!

You take Theo— I'll take care of these!

Do it!

Max!

Max!

FLASH

Awesome!
You're the man,
Max!

Pileziin!
Pileziin!

A Shadow
Spy!

It's going
to touch
Theo!

FLASH

We've worn them out now!

Noah, block up the crack in
the glass with some dirt.

Rebecca and Ilvanna, guard the entrance.

I'm going to look all the way around and make sure there's no way for the Shadow Spies to get in.

I think we're safe for the night. We need to get some sleep now.

SPLORTCH

What are we going to do about Theo? He's been out since morning.

Nothing. We can't do anything. We're just kids in a lost world.

Norgavol would know what to do.

We'll watch over him in shifts during the night. I'll go first. Then Rebecca and then Noah.

Ilvanna can take the last watch.

Ilvanna, wake up! It's your turn.

Gotta... get... sleep...

Ah!

Palaak!

Es teo Palaak?

THUMP

Up there!

NExt Episode...

the ElseWHERE CHRONICLES

BOOK THREE: THE MASTER OF SHADOWS

Art by Bannister
Story by Nykko
Colors by Jaffré
Translation by Carol Klio Burrell

First American edition published in 2009 by Graphic Universe™.
Published by arrangement with S.A. DUPUIS, Belgium.

Graphic Universe™
A division of Lerner Publishing Group, Inc.
241 First Avenue North
Minneapolis, MN 55401 USA

For reading levels and more information, look up this title at www.lernerbooks.com.

Library of Congress Cataloging-in-Publication Data

Bannister.
[Ombres. English]
The Shadow Spies / art by Bannister ; story by Nykko ; [colors by Jaffré ;
translation by Carol Klio Burrell]. — 1st American ed.
p.   cm. — (The ElseWhere chronicles ; bk. 2)
Summary: Rebecca, Max, Theo, and Noah continue their journey through the other world
in search of a way home, pursued by the Shadow Spies and the mysterious Master of Shadows.
ISBN: 978-0-7613-4460-5 (lib. bdg. : alk. paper)
1. Graphic novels. [1. Graphic novels. 2. Horror stories.] I. Nykko. II. Jaffré.
III. Burrell, Carol Klio. IV. Title.
PZ7.7.B34Sm 2009
741.5'973—dc22   2008039443

Manufactured in the United States of America
8-52418-10414-1/10/2022